Color Your Imagination Wild!

DesignScapes

MindWare®
www.MINDWAREonline.com

Color Your Imagination Wild!

This extraordinary coloring book offers one-of-a-kind patterns, textures and styles that you make your own by coloring each shape. Choose your method: markers, crayons or pencils, or pastels. Then let your vision take the lead for spectacular, colorful results.

Collect all four books—
ArchiScapes, DesignScapes, EnviroScapes and MasterScapes.

Try these other MindWare favorites!

Lights Stained Glass Coloring Books
Your color brings to life 16 original images printed on special transparent paper—watch the light burst through in SpinLights, EuroLights, TesseLights and EcoLights.

Designs Coloring Books
You're the creator with one-of-a-kind illustrations in PrismDesigns, UltraDesigns, GeoDesigns and OptiDesigns.

Mosaics Coloring Books
Explore ancient worlds through color! Awaken your imagination as you discover 23 original designs celebrated by ancient cultures— Aboriginal Mosaics, Aztec Mosaics, Celtic Mosaics and Classic Mosaics.

Shapes Activity Books
Pre-school creators discover the numbers, colors, shapes and patterns found in nature and everyday objects in these unique, educational activity books.

Squzzle Puzzles
Arrange the high-quality puzzle cards into a 9" square by matching all the objects. Theme packs include: Animal Babies, Around the World, Creature Kingdom, 3-D Scramblers, Illusions, Insect Infested, Optical Illusions, Play Ball! and World Money. Three different puzzles in each themed pack.

Handful Of Riddles
Picture and word clues help you solve 104 science or geography riddles. Cards and books include answers. Books are reproducible.

Bella's Mystery Card Decks
Help our 13-year-old heroine Bella solve 50 non-violent mysteries in each of these MindWare bestsellers. Three different titles now available.

Illustrations by Adam Turner

International Standard Book Number: ISBN 1-892069-20-2

This book may be ordered from the publisher.

MindWare® **Brainy Toys for Kids of All Ages**®
www.MINDWAREonline.com
1-800-999-0398

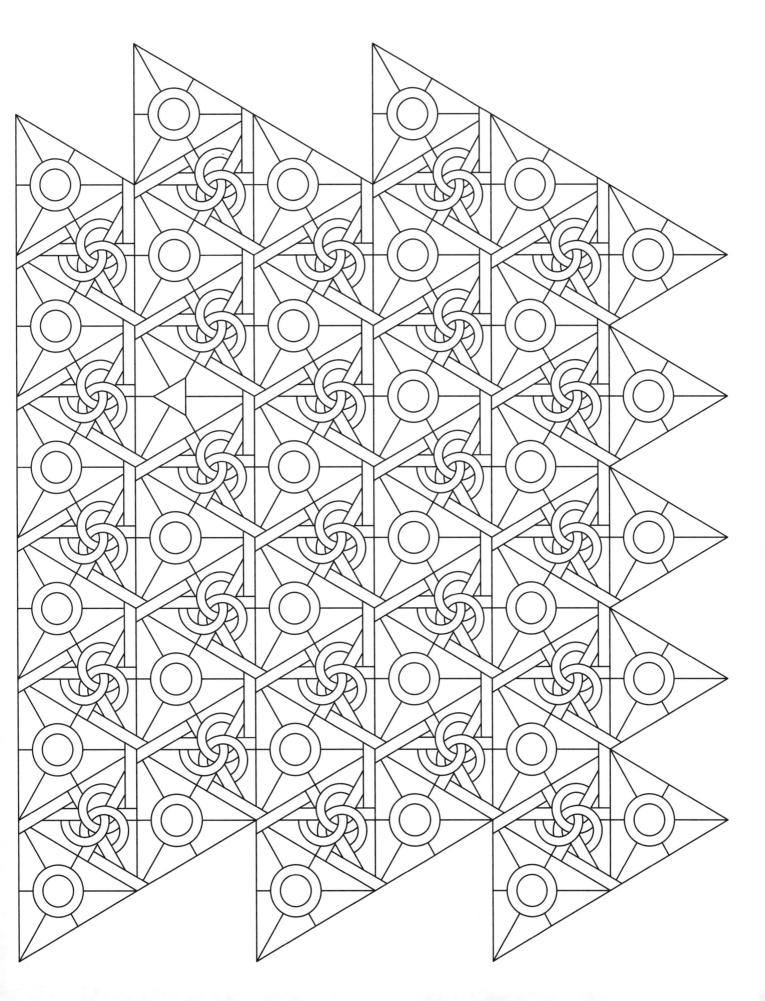

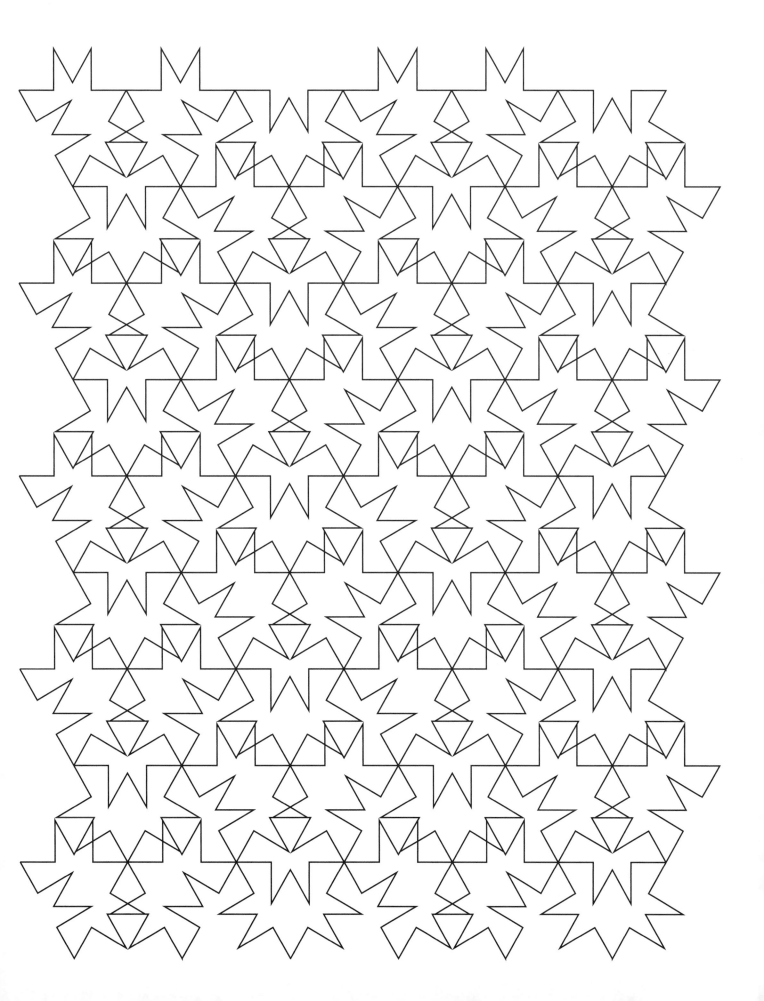

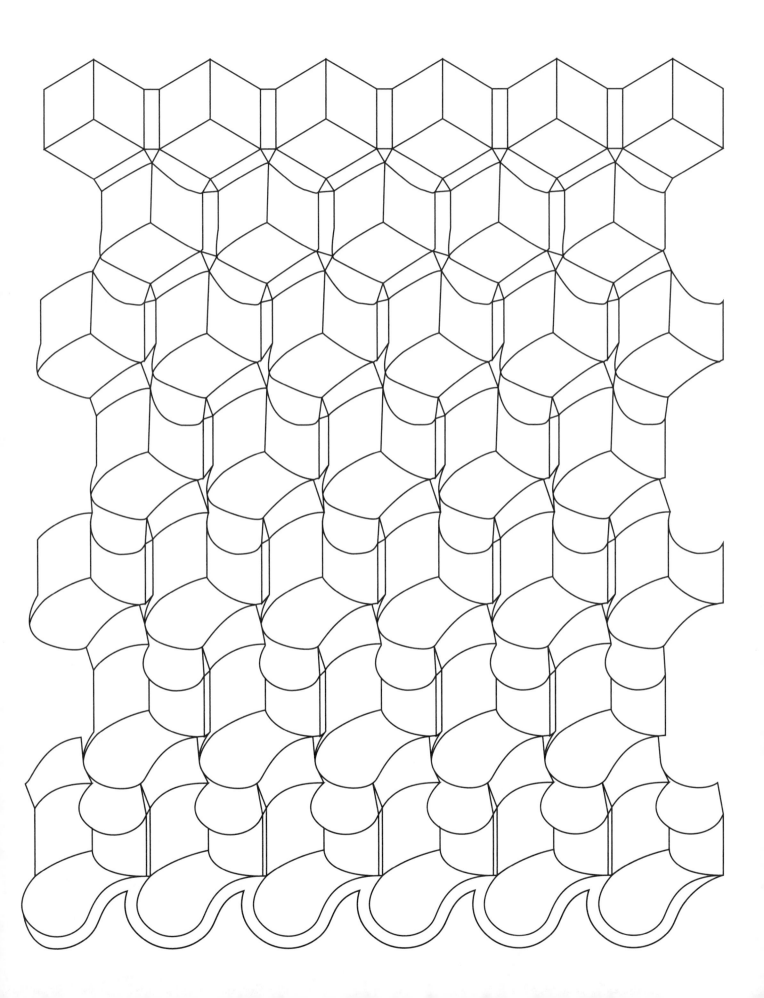

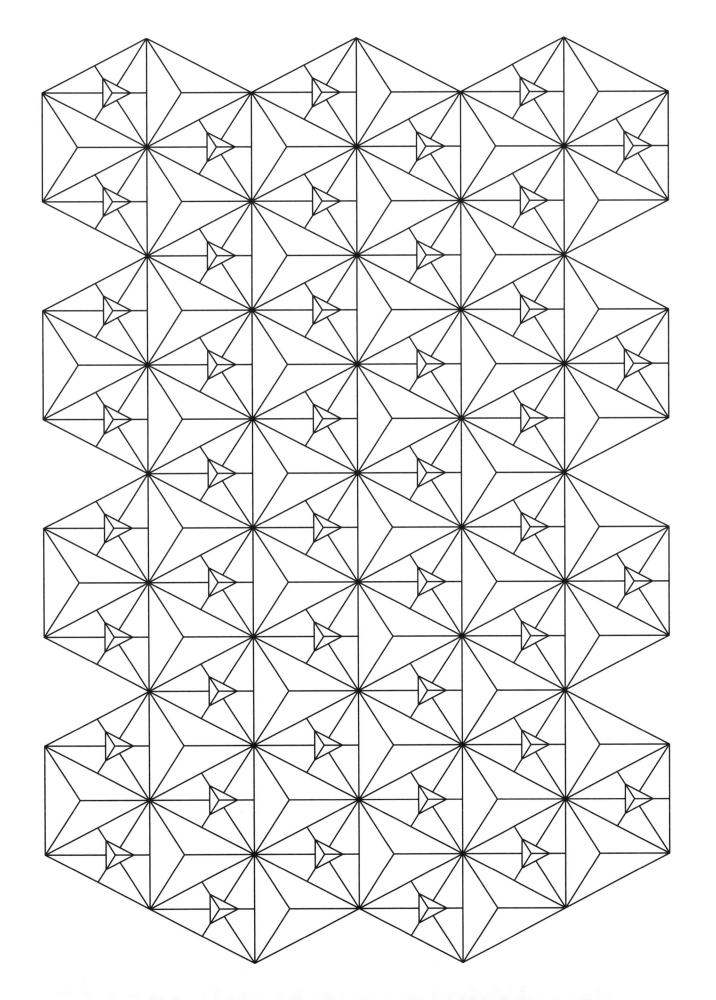

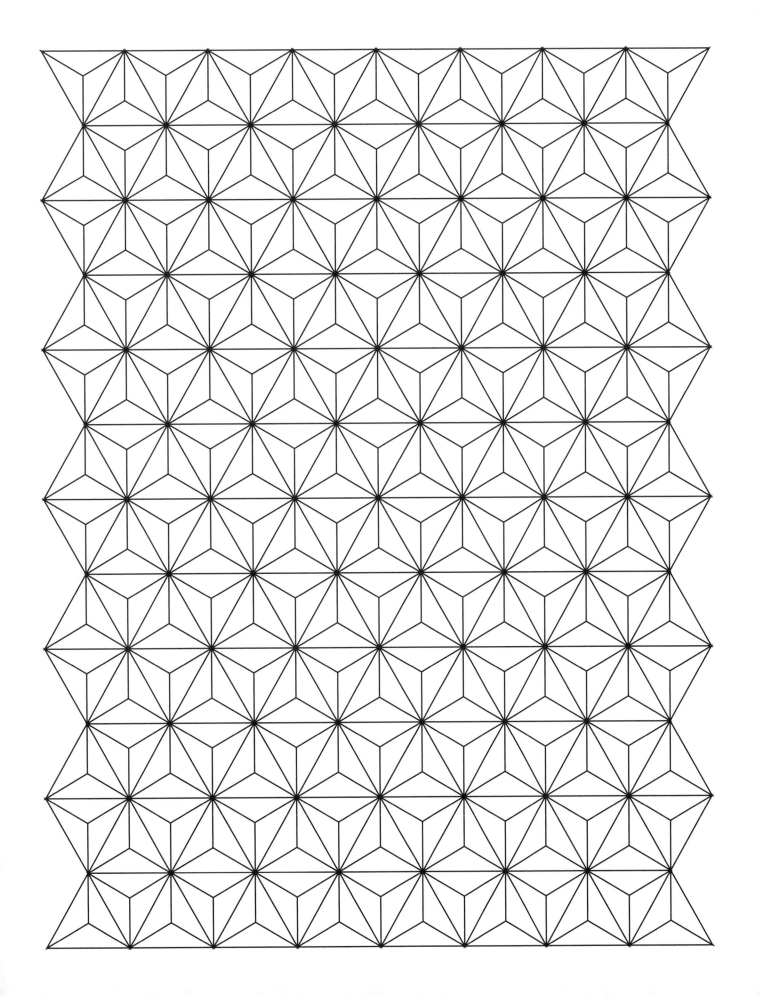

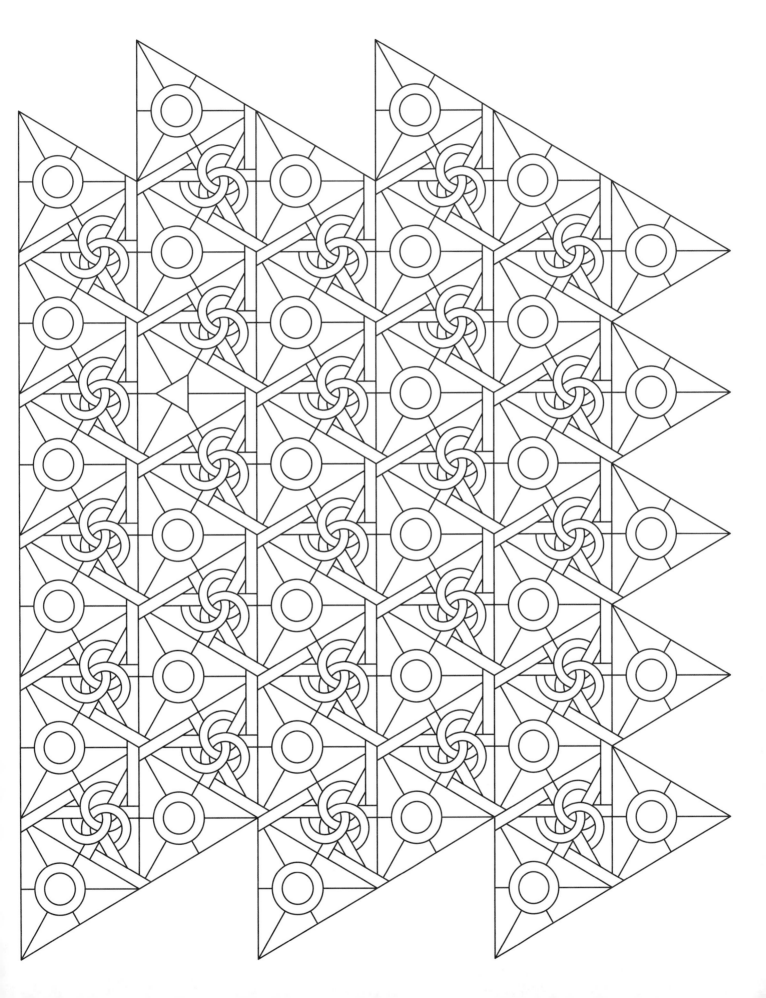

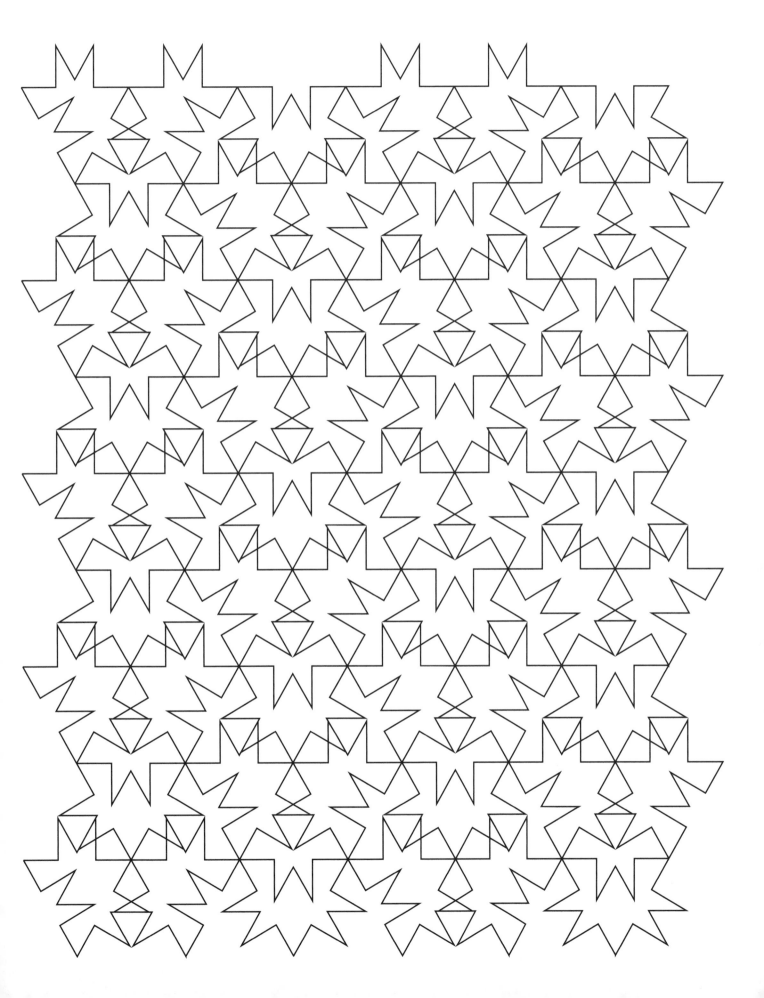

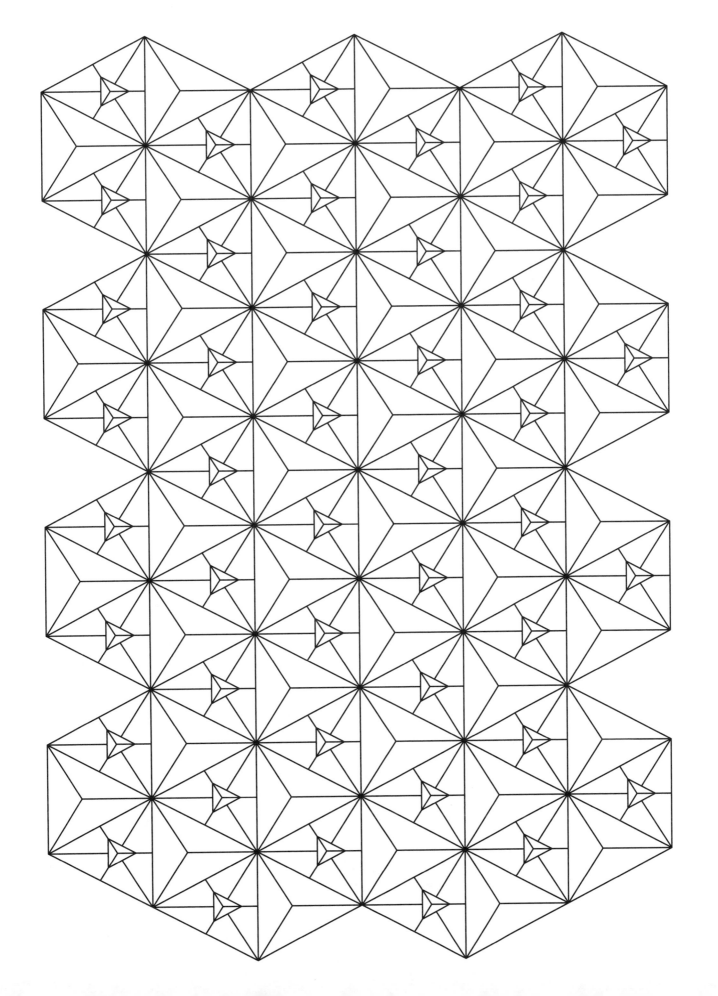

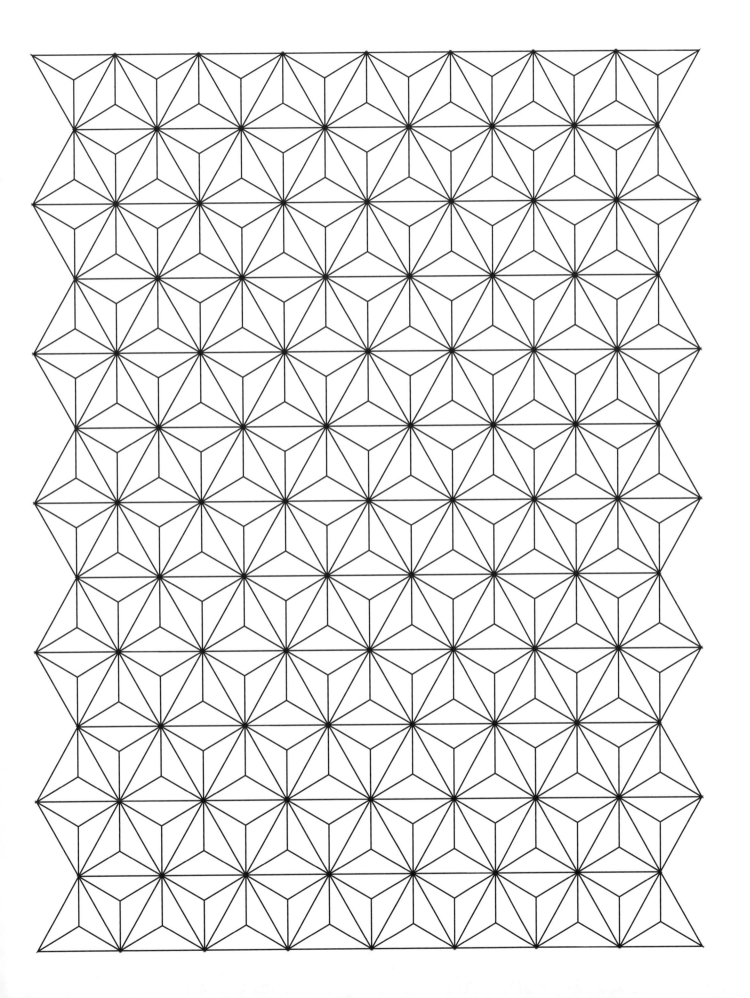